Contents

What is a pod?

Splash! Huge whales jump out of the water. Whales live together in groups. A group of whales is called a pod. Pods live in all the oceans.

About 3 to 50 whales live in a pod. Some pods have up to 100 whales. One female leads the pod. Other females and their young live in the pod.

7

Swimming together

A pod of whales travels from place to place. It swims to colder waters. The pod looks for food. It travels to warmer waters where females will give birth.

Females have one baby at a time. The baby is called a calf. Calves drink their mother's milk. They stay in the pod for several years.

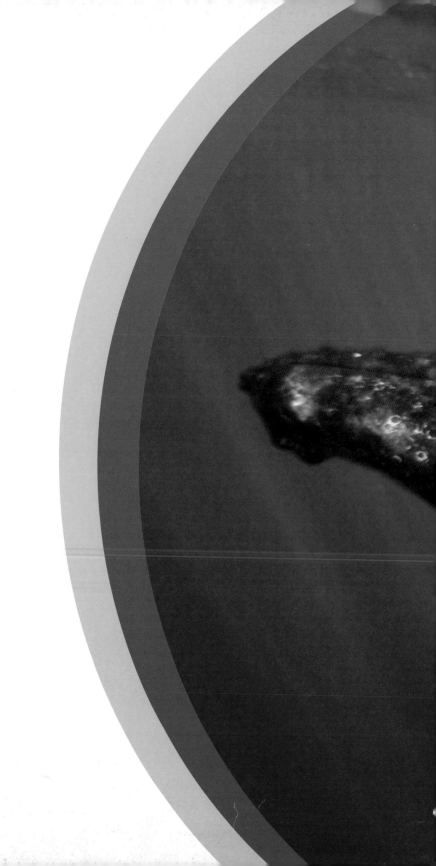

Young males leave the pod.

They look for mates.

Young females may explore outside their pod, but they usually return.

Time to eat!

Whales look for food. Some
whales eat plankton and
other small sea life. The whales
trap food with baleen.
Baleen are like teeth.

baleen

Some whales eat large sea animals. The whales make sounds that bounce off objects. This helps them to find their prey. They swallow it whole.

Whale talk

Whales jump out of the water. This is called breaching. The jump can tell other whales to change direction. Whales also breach to see what is around them.

Whales sing too. They sing
to find mates. They also make
clicks and whistles.
Whales slap their tails.
This warns others of danger.

Glossary

baleen long, fringed plates in the mouths of some whales

breach jump out of the water

calf young whale

mate one of a pair of animals that join together to produce young

plankton tiny plants and animals that drift in the ocean

prey animal hunted by another animal for food

Find out more

Books

Save the Humpback Whale (Animal SOS), Louise Spilsbury (Raintree, 2020)

Shark vs Killer Whale (Animal Rivals), Isabel Thomas (Raintree, 2018)

When Whales Cross the Sea: The Grey Whale Migration (Extraordinary Migrations), Sharon Katz Cooper (Raintree, 2016)

Websites

www.bbc.co.uk/cbbc/quizzes/bp-whale-quiz
Take this quiz to test your whale knowledge!

www.dkfindout.com/uk/animals-and-nature/whales-dolphins-and-porpoises/what-is-whale
Find out more about whales.

Comprehension questions

1. Why do pods travel?
2. What are the two different ways that whales find food?
3. What is breaching? Why do whales breach?

Index